A Handy Dragon

Some people travel
by bus.
Some people travel
by plane.

Some people travel
by car.
Some people travel
by train.

But when I want to travel,
I say,

"I travel by dragon.
It's by far the best way."

Some people toast
by oven.
Some people toast
by flame.

Some people toast
by toaster.
It all tastes
just the same.

But when I want
to have toast, I say,

"I toast by dragon.
It's by far the best way."

Some people make soup
in a cup.
Some people make soup
in a pot.

Some people make soup
by microwave
and make it
nice and hot.

But when I want
to make soup, I say,

"I make it by dragon.
It's by far the best way."

Some people carry
flashlights
when they go out at night.

Some people carry
lanterns
and some have candlelight.

But when I go out
at night, I say,
"I go by dragon.
It's by far the best way."